A CENTURY OF PIANO MUSIC

TWENTY-ONE BRITISH PIANO WORKS OF THE TWENTIETH CENTURY

GRADES 5-7

SELECTED AND EDITED BY RICHARD DEERING

BOSWORTH

Music settings by Enigma Music Production Services

BOE005126
ISMN: M2016 4056-3

This compilation © 2000 Bosworth & Co. Ltd.
Published in Great Britain by Bosworth and Company Limited

Head office: 14-15 Berners Street,
London W1T 3LJ, UK.

Tel: +44 (0)20 7434 0066
Fax: +44 (0)20 7287 6329

Sales and Hire:
Music Sales Distribution Centre,
Newmarket Road,
Bury St. Edmunds,
Suffolk IP33 3YB

Tel: +44 (0)1284 702600
Fax: +44 (0)1284 768301

www.musicsales.com
e-mail: music@musicsales.co.uk

Television and on-stage performances throughout the world
have won Richard Deering a reputation as one of Britain's
leading – and most entertaining – soloists and lecture recitalists.
He studied in London with Frank Merrick and Peter Wallfisch.
His engagements, which have been in remote villages as well as
major cities, have taken him to more than ninety countries.
Recognised as an authority on British music through his lectures,
concerts, broadcasts, recordings and writings, he has been entrusted
with many first performances by leading composers, including
Malcolm Arnold, Thomas Wilson, Edward Gregson, Edward McGuire,
Charles Camilleri and Brian Chapple. Many composers have written
specially for him and he has commissioned several new works. He is
also a noted accompanist, teacher and examiner and has served on
competition juries throughout the British Isles as well as in Canada,
South Africa, Hong Kong and New Zealand.

PREFACE

If the first golden age of British musical creativity may be said to have ended with the death of Purcell in 1695, a second certainly began around the first years of the twentieth century. Edward Elgar, Gustav Holst, Frederick Delius and Hubert Parry initially, then Frank Bridge, John Ireland, Cyril Scott and Ralph Vaughan Williams broke upon the scene in a renaissance which led to a second half century full of originality, a wide diversity of ideas and an abundance of composers working in every conceivable musical medium. That creativity is nowhere more strikingly demonstrated than in the genre of works for piano solo. This collection, suitable for young and non-professional pianists, celebrates a century of rediscovered musical vitality.

As an aid to preparation and interpretation, there is a short explanatory paragraph on each piece. Generally, fingering has been added, though not in pieces where several alternatives would be viable. Some of the fingering problems connected with certain pieces are discussed in the respective performance notes. When choosing your fingering, be conscious of phrase shape and the need to contour the natural accents of the phrases. As far as possible, aim to achieve legato effects with your fingering, only using the pedal for colouring and prescribed effects. I have also indicated essential pedalling but student and teacher must realise that additional pedalling will be needed in line with conventional pedal application to aid the tonal resonance and rhythmic framework, especially the harmonic rhythm.

Always remember that musical notation is only a guide to performance. Observe all markings, of course, but add some imagination to bring a piece to life and realise what the composer is trying to convey. Use the title and any other pictorial illusions within the piece to help you realise the mood and sound but also try to understand what is happening within the actual music. Aim to understand how the composer has constructed his composition and appreciate the significance and emotive effect of certain notes, harmonies or modulations.

I hope that you all enjoy learning and playing these hand picked works as much as I did. They represent the width, breadth and quality of British music of the twentieth century.

Richard Deering
1st January 2000

CONTENTS

NOTES

Old Musical Box Eugène Goossens p. 2

Notice the instruction to keep both pedals down throughout, and, if the articulation is clear enough and sufficiently crisp and soft, there is no need to change the sustaining pedal at all. The R.H. finger work needs to be very staccato with crushed grace-notes, but remember also that the ostinato L.H. is detached throughout, too.

Hurdy-Gurdy Man Eugène Goossens p.4

Underline the rhythm by using short pedals on each downbeat and then shifting that technique when the beat becomes displaced in the middle section. Always be conscious of the melody's shape above the chords; think of the linear shaping as well as the vertical synchronisation of the chordings.

Suburban Sunday Philip Lane p.6

Aim for a gently rocking L.H. part with the hand pivoting in a rotary fashion around the 2nd or 3rd finger, whichever it is that suits, for the playing of the second note in each L.H. figure. Aim to play the 5th fingers well onto the keys – almost touching the black keys – and then rotary action will be controlled. Avoid unnecessary accents in either hand but feel the gentle stresses on the natural beats of each bar. In the passage where the tune is shared between the alto and tenor parts, balance the hands so that the weight is towards the thumbs.

Water-Pearls William Baines p.8

An exciting rhythmic drive established by the L.H. staccatos and slurs forms the foundation here for a light but brightly articulated R.H. Depress all the keys fully to achieve the ringing effect – never confuse lightness of depression with softness as the key depression must be consistent whatever the dynamic marking.

Black on White (Zebra Music 10) Giles Swayne p.11

Avoid any suggestion of sustaining, with either fingers or feet, apart from the clearly marked tenuto notes and later smooth section. Even in those passages, resist the temptation to use any kind of pedalling. The R.H. playing black notes throughout and the L.H white, be very clear about the character contrasts.

Mazurka No.1 Lennox Berkeley p.12

Written as homage to Chopin, this piece moves from reflective to exuberant but never should the prevailing rhythm be compromised. If some of the stretches are too great, experiment with sharing notes between the hands before you decide to affect the rhythm by spreading a chord. In bar 23, for example, I play the third beat tenor B in the R.H. and in bar 8, I would do likewise on the third beat, but here so as to help the L.H. balance before the journey down to the following low octave.

Concertina Cyril Scott p.15

In principle, this piece is not difficult. If, however, a highly developed wrist action has not become part of the technique, the phrasing and nuances here will be difficult to achieve. Drop the wrist on the beats and catch the softer chord of each couplet while the wrist is moving back upwards, like a regular gentle kneading or rebounding process. Let your wrist movements simulate the squeezing and releasing of the actual concertina.

Prelude No.2 Christopher Headington p.16

A relaxed and lyrical R.H. line needs to be supported by a firm bass line movement of crotchets. Always remember to observe the nuances in the L.H. as well as in the melody. Generally, crotchet pedals will suffice throughout, but in passages such as bars 4-5 you may have to experiment with half-pedalling. All depends on the sonority, volume and balance as often when pedalling seems blurred, it is a problem more within the balance of the playing than with the actual pedal work.

The Artful Dodger John McCabe p.18

The title is self-explanatory and the effect is achieved though well proportioned dynamics, crisp finger work in the runs with rhythmic stress upon the first note of each group of semiquavers thereby underlining the strong beat. Despite the staccato markings on the opening chords, ensure that the note length is greater than the intervening gap. As a general rule, accept that staccato makes a note seven-eighths of its principal values and not over detached. Observe the phrasing very carefully as the considerable detail in this piece creates the character perfectly and solves all interpretation problems for everyone.

Game of Darts John McCabe p.20

Right from the early stages of note learning, become used to maintaining an absolutely regular pulse. Initially practice in four-a-bar so that the small rests become clear and precise. Also from the early stages, be conscious of the dynamic proportions. Never just learn notes and timing with the other features superimposed later because the learning process and character defining will always be longer unless everything has been absorbed together albeit at a slower tempo.

Christmas Past Judith Bingham p 22

The detailed dynamic and pedal markings are the main clues to a successful performance, but it is essential to explore a range of colourings and touches within the piece. Think in main beats throughout and never in six, because the transition from triplet to duplet divisions of the beat will then sound natural.

Cradle Song Kenneth Leighton p.24

Apart from the obvious problems of controlling the legato melody and the uniformity of tone as the melody switches from one hand to the other, the main difficulty here is in articulating clearly the little accompanying motif. Total control over the independence of the weaker fingers is essential here, so work at the dexterity exercises so as to increase that control.

Four Calling Birds Richard Rodney Bennett p.26

An approach similar to that needed for playing many of the early Satie pieces is needed here – bar-long pedals, a precise depression of the keys with controlled soft colourings and a keen awareness of the pulse through the minims. It works equally well if the grace notes are hurried or if they are relaxed – maybe you could incorporate a mixture of both approaches – but beware of confusing them with the Scotch-snap rhythm of bar 14 and elsewhere.

Miriam's Music Michael Ball p.28

Be careful not to confuse the boisterous character with harshness and aggression. Relax the arm into the fortissimo chords and enjoy the tonal substance and sustaining quality thereby achieved. In the opening passage, keep the arm buoyant so that the rhythmic propulsion is maintained with two beats to a bar and not four. Pay particular attention to the slurs, staccatos and accents as they are not always quite predictable making the piece far more interesting as a result.

All Alone Robert Walker p.30

Firmness of key depression is absolutely essential here. Remember that dynamic contrasts are achieved through the speed of key depression and not through the weight. Consequently, if the soft nature of this piece persuades you to depress the keys timidly you will experience inconsistencies of tone and balance, and, most probably, have several non-sounding notes within the chordings. The ability to play softly and guarantee clarity and guarantee that all of the notes speak is one of the most important skills for a pianist to acquire. Generally, you can pedal dotted crotchet beats throughout this piece.

The Symbol at Your Door Robert Walker p.32

Do the glissandi with the back of the R.H., using the nails, but not at too acute an angle as you will scrape the knuckle skin or have blood coming from around your cuticles! Let the L.H. follow the R.H. up the glissandi for balance and for playing the top notes of the glissando rhythmically. The black note glissandos need a little experimenting with as they can be easier if played lower down below the knuckles, but much will depend upon the action tension of the piano in question.

Secret Song No.6 Peter Maxwell Davies p.34

The long arching melodic line, covering the entire keyboard, with very little direct harmonic support is a keen test of any player's imagination. Strive for complete smoothness using two hands throughout, if that helps the stretches and to avoid disturbing accents punctuating the line unnecessarily. Never feel restricted to using just the R.H. for material on the upper stave, nor the L.H. alone on the lower stave; if a hand is experiencing difficulty in any form and the other hand is free, share the material. The dramatic nuances need careful planning in this piece, and feel free to experiment with pedal in places other than where marked so as to underline the harmonic implications of the angular line.

Elegiac Blues Constant Lambert p.35

Although this piece needs to sound ponderous and lugubrious it must neither drag nor be too slow. As indicated, the L.H. chords need to be spread slightly, almost as of playing then with a bad technique. Make the crotchet triplets hold back but, otherwise, the detailed markings achieve the effects if observed scrupulously.

5 Miniature Pieces, No.5 Edward McGuire p.38

Exploit the fun and unexpected twists to the full but never let it become heavy handed.

Trembling Leaves Stanley Glasser p.40

Notice the tempo changes and the moving from free time to a strict pulse. Make sure that the extreme dynamic contrasts are clear to the listener.

Water-Wagtail Cyril Scott p.42

This piece has been a favourite of many for generations and is probably the best known composition in this collection. Aim for a relaxed and sweetly singing style of playing with a controlled rubato at phrase ends and awkward melodic twists guaranteeing the carefree sense of the outer sections. Use long pedals to retain the harmonic rhythm, which involves pedalling for the first seven bars as two bars - one bar - one bar - one bar - one bar, and the individual beats. The middle section, although more intense, does not want to be too dry, despite the staccato marings. Again, the harmonic rhythm needs to be clear when deciding upon your pedalling here.

The Old Musical Box

Op.18 No.8

Eugène Goosens

Leggiero ♩ = 110

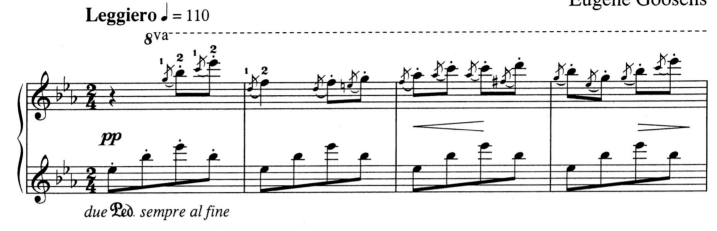

pp

due Ped. sempre al fine

simile

p

mf leggiero

pp

Int. Copyright Secured

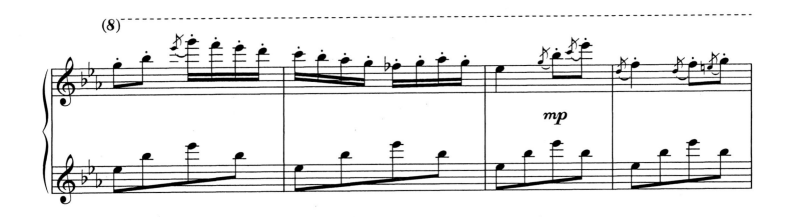

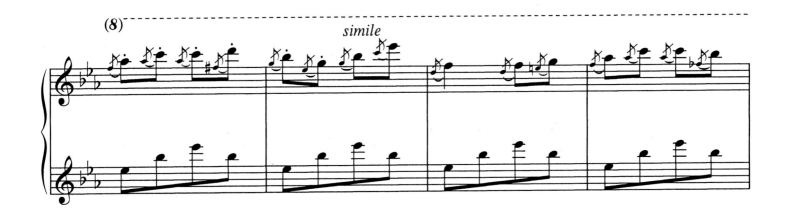

The Hurdy-Gurdy Man

Op.18 No.3

Tempo di Valse ♩. = 72

Eugène Goosens

Suburban Sunday

from *Leisure Lanes* (1982)

Philip Lane

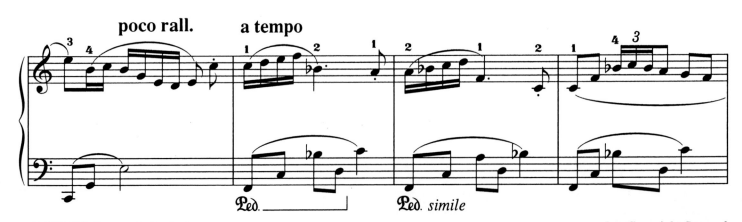

Water-Pearls

from *Silverpoints* (1921)

William Baines

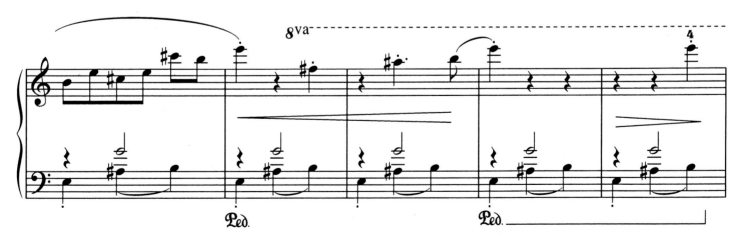

9

Black on White

No.10 *Zebra Music* (1993)

Giles Swayne

Mazurka No. 1

from *Three Mazurkas ("Hommage à Chopin")* (1951)

Lennox Berkeley

14

Concertina

from *For My Young Friends* (1920)

Cyril Scott

Int. Copyright Secured

Prelude No. 2

from *Five Preludes* (1954)

Christopher Headington

17

The Artful Dodger

from *Afternoon and Afterwards* (1982)

John McCabe

19

A Game of Darts

from *Afternoons and Afterwards* (1982)

John McCabe

Vivo ♩ = c. 144

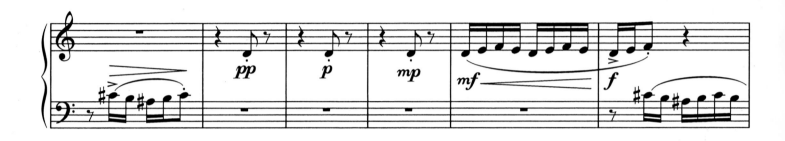

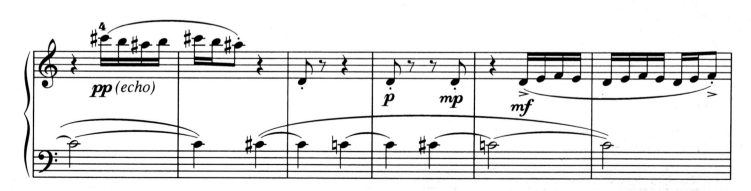

Christmas Past

from *Christmas Past, Christmas Present* (1991)

Judith Bingham

*take your time getting to the next chord: place it.

© 1991 Novello & Company Ltd.

Int. Copyright Secured

*Staccato marks on notes sustained by pedal imply a lightness of touch.

Cradle-Song

from *Pieces for Angela*, Op. 47 (1967)

Non troppo lento, dolce

Kenneth Leighton

Int. Copyright Secured

Four Calling Birds

from *Partridge Pie* Book 1 (1991)

Richard Rodney Bennett

Miriam's Music

Boisterously ♩ = c.200 [♪ = ♪ throughout]

Michael Ball

Int. Copyright Secured

hold back
slightly

All Alone

from *Twelve-O* (1974)

Robert Walker

Very slow and sustained (adagio sostenuto)

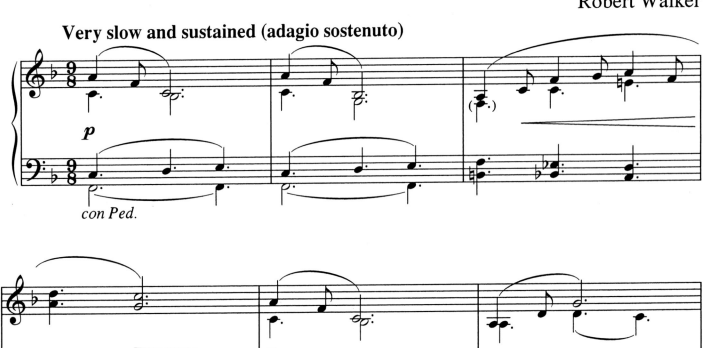

con Ped.

con Ped.

Int. Copyright Secured

The Symbol at Your Door

from *Twelve-O* (1974)

Robert Walker

Six Secret Songs

No.6

Peter Maxwell Davies

Elegiac Blues

Lugubre ma con moto

Constant Lambert

Int. Copyright Secured

5 Miniature Pieces

No. 5

Edward McGuire

39

Trembling Leaves

Stanley Glasser

Water-Wagtail

Op.71 No.3

Cyril Scott

7/08 (166379)